This book is dedicated to my sons, Milo and Shay. Thank you for inspiring me to become a Family Sleep Specialist, for listening to me talk about the importance of sleep every single day of your lives, and for helping me to write this book. I love you both very much!

ISBN-13: 978-1-7326823-1-3

Devin & Evan series, Volume 1

Copyright © 2018 by Whitney Roban

This is a story of Devin & Evan,

Twin brothers and the best of friends.

They share a love of so many things,

But sleep is where all that ends.

Devin gets 11 hours of sleep,

He sleeps from 8-7.

His brother gets only 8 hours of sleep,

That's not enough sleep for Evan.

Devin loves how sleep makes him feel,

From his toes right up to his head.

So, when it's time to go to sleep,

He can't wait to get into bed.

Devin says goodnight to his parents,

While happily singing a song.

He goes to sleep in his very own bed,

And that sleep will last all night long.

Evan never looks forward to bedtime,

For him it's not quite the same.

He won't listen to his parents,

And treats bedtime like it's a game.

When Evan finally falls asleep,

There's been yelling and some tears.

He refuses to sleep in his own bed,

He has not slept there in years.

Devin awakes with a huge smile,

As the big test day is here.

But sitting at the breakfast table,

On Evan's face there is only fear.

Evan awoke with a pain in his head,

His stomach ached a lot too.

He wasn't prepared to take the test,

And he didn't know what to do.

In class, Evan cannot focus,

He's always falling asleep.

He had trouble studying for the test,

And all he could do was weep.

Devin pays attention in class,

And all of the knowledge that he gains.

After he has a good night of sleep,

In his brain all the knowledge remains.

The teacher handed out the test,

For well rested Devin it was easy.

But Evan was so exhausted,

That the test made him feel queasy.

Devin received a well deserved 'A',

On his sleep and on the test.

But poor tired Evan got only a 'D',

Because he got so little rest.

The weekend was coming upon them,

Devin & Evan couldn't wait.

It was time for their friend's party,

They knew it was going to be great.

That morning, Devin woke up happy,

And feeling real healthy too.

He was all dressed and ready,

For the birthday party at the zoo.

Evan awoke on that morning,

With a high fever and feeling sick.

He had to go to the doctor again,

And this time he had to go quick.

Evan gets sick very often,

Due to the sleep he will not get.

He had to miss out on the party,

His tears made his whole face wet.

If Evan would go to bed early,

And if he would sleep all night.

He would get sick a whole lot less,

And his doctor would stay out of sight.

Without getting the sleep that he needs,

Evan will stay sick and sad.

With basketball tryouts coming up,

If he's not better it will be bad.

Basketball tryouts have arrived,

It is their favorite sport.

They could play it all day long,

Running up and down the court.

Devin's tryouts went really well,

He was fast and he ran a lot.

He played an excellent defensive game,

And he missed not a single shot.

Unfortunately for Evan,

He's not as fast, strong or tall.

That's why he didn't make the team,

He kept dropping the basketball.

If Evan would only get better sleep,

He'd be much faster on his feet.

Just like his twin brother Devin,

Who's a very well rested athlete.

One day, Evan finally realized,

Sleep is important in every way.

If he got good sleep like Devin,

He would feel great every day.

So, he agreed to an early bedtime,

He now loved his big boy bed.

He promised to follow every sleep rule,

And listened to all his parents said.

Evan's grades improved in school,

He got healthy, strong and fast.

He found he was so happy every day,

That he knew this great sleep would last.

Healthy sleep is as important,

As it is to eat healthy food.

When you get a good night's sleep,

You wake in a wonderful mood.

So, try to go to sleep early,

Instead of staying up late.

This is how you can be sure,

You will feel and do really great.

Good sleep will always make us,

Healthy, happy, smart and strong.

If you make sure to get enough sleep,

You know you cannot go wrong!

A Note to Parents and Teachers: Why is sleep so important?

Sleep is not a luxury; it's a necessity. We don't just want to sleep; we need to sleep. As human beings, we have the basic biological need to sleep, to eat and to breathe. Healthy sleep is just as important as having healthy food to eat and healthy air to breathe. Every person needs these to survive and thrive.

Sleep affects all aspects of our daily lives. In general, sleep deprivation negatively affects our physical, cognitive, emotional and behavioral well being. More specifically, it has a profound effect on our mood and temperament, our memory, performance, productivity, attention, concentration, problem-solving and processing speed, as well as our immune system and risk for chronic diseases such as heart disease, stroke, diabetes, cancer, and obesity. These negative consequences occur in both children and adults in the home, school, and workplace. There are just no positive results from sleep deprivation.

Most children are not taught about the importance of sleep, neither in the home nor at school. They are unaware of the benefits of sleep, as well as the detriments of sleep deprivation. Using examples from their everyday lives, the goal of this book is to teach children why sleep is so important. Once children understand the value of getting enough sleep, they will happily accept healthy sleep into their lives. Rest assured (no pun intended), it is never too late to teach children healthy sleep habits.

Wishing you all many long and peaceful nights of sleep!

Dr. Roban's Top 10 Family Sleep Tips

1. If you start EARLY teaching good sleep habits, you will PREVENT sleep problems. However, it is NEVER too late to acquire good sleep habits.

2. Age appropriate, early, and consistent sleep schedules and routines need to be ESTABLISHED and MAINTAINED for you and your child.

3. BRIEF and CONSISTENT sleep routines will decrease your family's anxiety. Children feel safe and comforted knowing what will occur at bedtime everyday.

4. The more RESTED your family is, the more everyone will ACCEPT sleep, EXPECT to sleep, and CRAVE sleep.

5. An EARLY BEDTIME is the only way to provide your family with ample time to get the required amount of sleep they need and deserve.

6. Sleep deprivation causes adults to appear exhausted, but children to appear "wired" and not tired at all. The MORE TIRED a person is, the HARDER it is to fall asleep and stay asleep.

7. Sleep assisted by parents and/or electronics does NOT produce good quality sleep. We all need to learn to fall asleep and get back to sleep ON OUR OWN.

8. Healthy sleep is as IMPORTANT as a healthy diet. They are both MEDICAL issues for children and adults.

9. Healthy sleep improves MOOD, TEMPERAMENT, BEHAVIOR, IMMUNE SYSTEM, COGNITIVE DEVELOPMENT, and PERFORMANCE. The benefits of healthy sleep are endless.

10. In order to get the Zzzz's, follow the ABC's (ASSERTIVENESS, BELIEF in yourself and your child, and COMMITMENT to healthy sleep).

About the Author

Dr. Whitney Roban considers sleep a necessity, not a luxury, and has helped thousands of families sleep soundly every night. Through her various family, educational, and corporate sleep programs, Dr. Roban provides the education, solutions and support parents need to have well-rested families, students need to have academic success, working parents need to thrive both at home and at work, and corporations need to have healthy and well-rested employees. With a Ph.D. in Clinical and School Psychology, Dr. Roban's unique and invaluable education, training, and experience as a clinical and school psychologist paved the way to her success as a leading expert in family sleep.